PRAISE FOR
THE GOAL: A BUSINESS GRAPHIC NOVEL

ELIYAHU M. GOLDRATT'S

THE GOAL

A BUSINESS GRAPHIC NOVEL

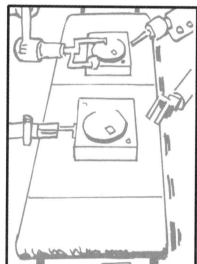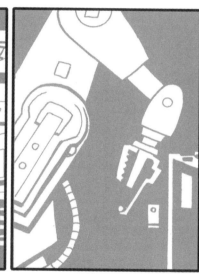

BASED ON THE BUSINESS NOVEL,
THE GOAL: A PROCESS OF ONGOING IMPROVEMENT
BY ELIYAHU M. GOLDRATT
AND JEFF COX

North River Press

The North River Press
Publishing Corporation
P.O. Box 567
Great Barrington, MA 01230
(800) 486.2665 or (413) 528.0034
www.northriverpress.com

for more information regarding the ideas
presented in this book go to www.goldrattconsulting.com

ISBN: 978-0-88427-207-6

This is a Z File, Inc. Book

Script by Dwight Jon Zimmerman
Interior art and design by Dean Motter
Cover illustration by Dean Motter
Graphic Assistance by Courtney Remillared
Edited by Howard Zimmerman

AN INTRODUCTION TO THE THEORY OF CONSTRAINTS

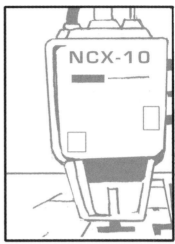

ADAPTED BY DWIGHT JON ZIMMERMAN

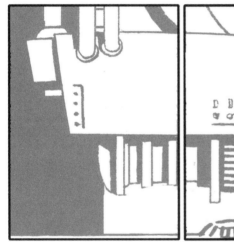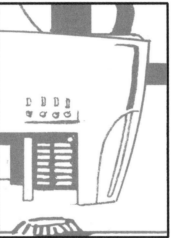

ILLUSTRATED BY DEAN MOTTER

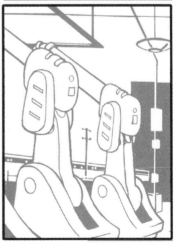

DEVELOPED AND EDITED BY HOWARD ZIMMERMAN

ABOUT ELIYAHU M. GOLDRATT

ELIYAHU M. GOLDRATT was an Israeli physicist and the father of the Theory of Constraints (TOC). He has been heralded as a "guru to industry" by *Fortune Magazine* and called "a genius" by *Business Week*. His first business novel, *The Goal*, has been a bestseller since 1984. With more than 7 million copies sold worldwide, it is recognized as one of the best-selling business books of all time. He authored many other books, including the business novels, *It's Not Luck* (the sequel to *The Goal*), *Critical Chain*, *Necessary but Not Sufficient* and *Isn't It Obvious?*. Dr. Goldratt was the founder of Goldratt Consulting (www.goldrattconsulting.com) and TOC for Education, a nonprofit organization dedicated to bringing TOC Thinking and TOC tools to teachers and their students (www.tocforeducation.com).

ABOUT THE SCRIPTER

DWIGHT JON ZIMMERMAN is a New York Times bestselling author and editor. He has written more than a dozen books, including *Lincoln's Last Days*, the New York Times bestselling adaptation of *Killing Lincoln*. He has written more than 300 articles on military history, as well as comic book stories for Marvel Comics and other comic book publishers.

ABOUT THE ARTIST

As art director and designer for CBS Records, Byron Preiss Visual Publications and DC Comics, illustrator DEAN MOTTER has created a plethora of award-winning book and record jackets. As a graphic novelist he is best known for *Terminal City*, *The Prisoner*, *Batman: Nine Lives* and his seminal creation, *Mister X*. He has illustrated nonfiction comic books for the Davis S. Wyman Institute and the Los Angeles Holocaust Museum, including *The Book Hitler Didn't Want You to Read* and *Karski's Mission: To Stop the Holocaust*.

INTRODUCTION

When my father, Dr. Eli Goldratt, started developing the Theory of Constraints, he decided to use a book to introduce its first application. He knew that many people didn't like reading boring management books. He thought he had an answer, he would write a story, a business novel or as some say a teaching novel. He was confident that publishers would welcome his book with open arms, but to his surprise, he got one rejection after another. One publisher was kind enough to explain: "If you want to write a novel, write a novel, if you want to write a business book, write a business book. But a business book that is written as a novel? We wouldn't even know what shelf to put it on." The tenth publisher he approached was Larry Gadd from The North River Press. Larry was an established publisher who published only books he believed in. He recognized the potential in the book and regardless of the fact that, at that time, there were no other business novels, he thought the risk was worth it. "People will enjoy a good story that they can also learn from," he said. The millions of copies *The Goal* sold, proved he got it right. That was over 30 years ago. I was just a kid.

Nowadays, more and more people don't like to read books at all. They have become accustomed to absorbing information in fast paced bits and bytes and reading is just too slow. *The Goal* is as relevant a book as it was decades ago, but the text format may discourage many from reading it. As the person in charge of my father's books I thought I may have a solution he would have been happy with. How about turning *The Goal* into a graphic novel? People raised an eyebrow. They said that if I want to publish comics, I should write comics but a business novel that is transformed to comics? Speaking of déjà vu... I turned to The North River Press, my father's long time publisher. Once again, Larry Gadd was enthusiastic. He recognized a new and greater potential for the still successful book he has been publishing for over thirty years, and regardless of the fact that there aren't many other business graphic novels around, he thought the risk was worth it. "You know, people will enjoy a story that they can also learn from." Larry accepted the challenge. He put together a team and we got to work. Did we get it right? You will be the judge of that.

Efrat Goldratt-Ashlag

THE GOAL

A BUSINESS GRAPHIC NOVEL

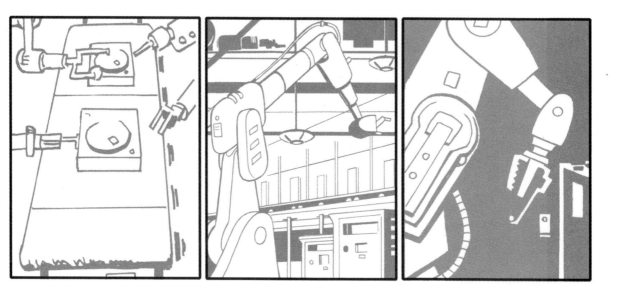

2

AL, I STILL THINK YOU CAN TURN THINGS AROUND.

YOU WILL GET BUCKY'S ORDER OUT TODAY, RIGHT?

WE'LL SHIP IT, BILL.

GOOD.

CLICK

IT'S BEEN A LONG DAY AND THE WORK IS NOT OVER YET. I NEED TO GET OUT OF HERE AND GET SOMETHING TO EAT.

HOW DID EVERYTHING GO SO WRONG SO FAST? SIX MONTHS AGO I WAS THE GOLDEN BOY--THE SAVIOR OF BEARINGTON'S UNICO PLANT. "HOMETOWN BOY RETURNS TO SAVE TOWN."

THE KIDS ARE DOING WELL IN SCHOOL. JULIE FINALLY TOOK THE BIG STEP AND OPENED HER OWN COMPANY. NOW IT'S TAKING OFF, AND *I'M* THE ONE WHO'S GROPING FOR ANSWERS.

LIKE BEARINGTON ITSELF...MY BETTER DAYS ARE BECOMING A DISTANT MEMORY.

THAT COMPANY USED TO EMPLOY 2,000 WORKERS. NOW IT'S AN EMPTY CARCASS.

SO MANY LOCAL BUSINESSES ARE BOARDED UP... MAYBE UNICO'S TIME IS UP, TOO?

RIGHT--I'LL JUST LET THE PLANT FOLD, AND PUT ANOTHER THOUSAND OUT OF WORK, PEOPLE WHO ARE *DEPENDING* ON ME.

HELL, *MOM* IS STILL LIVING OFF OF DAD'S UNICO PENSION.

ROGO RESIDENCE, 6:30 P.M.

NO, ROGO-- FAILURE IS NOT AN OPTION.

I'LL GRAB A BITE...MAYBE SOME COLD CHICKEN... AND HEAD BACK TO THE PLANT TO GET THAT ORDER OUT.

JULIE...

OHMIGOD, JULIE. IS THAT *TONIGHT?*

WHY-- WHAT'S WRONG?

BILL PEACH SHOWED UP TODAY--THEY'RE TALKING ABOUT CLOSING THE PLANT DOWN.

AND THERE'S A RUSH ORDER FROM ONE OF OUR BEST CUSTOMERS, PLUS A CRITICAL PIECE OF EQUIPMENT JUST WENT DOWN.

I'VE GOT TO--

HI, AL! WHAT A DAY. I DROPPED THE KIDS OFF WITH MY MOM ON THE WAY TO MY LAST CLIENT MEETING.

SO WE'RE ALL SET FOR OUR BIG "NIGHT ALONE."

I KNOW. YOU'VE GOT TO GO BACK AND MAKE SURE THE ORDER GETS OUT.

HONEY, YOU'RE THE BEST.

GO. I'LL JUST WATCH A MOVIE.

7

BACK AT THE PLANT, GETTING ORDER #41427 OUT THE DOOR IS ROGO'S SOLE PRIORITY.

HI, BOB. ARE WE GOING TO MAKE IT ON THE 41427 ORDER?

UH, WE'RE DOING OUR BEST.

BOB, ARE WE GOING TO SHIP THE ORDER TONIGHT, OR NOT?

MAYBE.

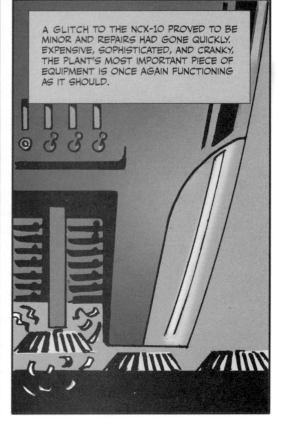

A GLITCH TO THE NCX-10 PROVED TO BE MINOR AND REPAIRS HAD GONE QUICKLY. EXPENSIVE, SOPHISTICATED, AND CRANKY, THE PLANT'S MOST IMPORTANT PIECE OF EQUIPMENT IS ONCE AGAIN FUNCTIONING AS IT SHOULD.

AS EACH FINISHED PIECE FOR ORDER 41427 COMES OUT, IT IS FITTED IN PLACE--

--AND ADJUSTED.

IT IS THEN HAND CARRIED TO THE NEXT STAGE OF ASSEMBLY. CLEARLY, NOT THE MOST *EFFICIENT* USE OF MEN AND MACHINES...

...BUT, IT GETS THE JOB DONE.

11:00 pm

CONGRATS, BOB.

THANKS, AL, BUT DON'T ASK ME HOW WE DID IT.

EVERY SIX
MONTHS, SOME
GROUP FROM *CORPORATE*
CREATES THE NEXT BIG
IDEA--THE LATEST
PANACEA FOR OUR
PROBLEMS...

SOMETHING
IS WRONG. I
DON'T KNOW *WHAT*
IT IS, BUT SOMETHING
VERY BASIC IS WRONG.
I'M CLEARLY MISSING
SOMETHING.

NONE DOES
ANY GOOD. WE LIMP
ALONG...NEVER GETTING
ANY BETTER...MOSTLY
GETTING *WORSE.*

WE'VE GOT
THE TECHNOLOGY;
SOME OF THE *BEST*
MACHINES MONEY
CAN BUY.

WE'VE GOT
STATE-OF-THE-ART
ROBOTICS.

COMPETITION'S
KILLING US.

THREE
YEARS AGO
WE GOT BEAT OUT
ON QUALITY AND DESIGN.
NOW IT'S PRICE AND
DELIVERIES.

WE'VE
GOT GOOD
PEOPLE--FOR THE
MOST PART. NO REAL
PROBLEMS WITH
THE UNION.

114 DAYS
WITHOUT
ACCIDENT

AND
WE'VE GOT
A *MARKET.*
SO?

UNICO CORPORATE HEADQUARTERS 7:50 A.M.

INSTEAD OF ATTENDING THIS *DIVISION PRODUCTIVITY* MEETING, I SHOULD BE DOING SOMETHING MORE PRODUCTIVE...

...LIKE PRODUCING PRODUCT!

AH, WELL, MINE IS NOT TO REASON WHY--

AL! AL ROGO!

WELL, IF IT ISN'T *NATHAN SELWIN*-- CONGRATULATIONS ON YOUR PROMOTION TO PEACH'S STAFF.

THANKS. BUT I'M NOT SO SURE HOW *GOOD* THE NEWS ACTUALLY IS.

IF PEACH DOESN'T TURN THINGS AROUND BY *THE END OF THE YEAR*, WORD IS THE DIVISION GOES UP FOR SALE...

...AND PEACH GOES WITH IT.

...TWO WEEKS EARLIER. O'HARE AIRPORT, CHICAGO.

HEY! THAT LOOKS LIKE...

JONAH?

DO I KNOW YOU?

IT'S ALEX ROGO.

I WAS A STUDENT OF YOURS, STUDYING MATHEMATICAL MODELS YOU WERE WORKING ON. I HAD A BEARD BACK THEN.

FUNNY, MY PLAN WAS TO BE A RESEARCHER. NOW I'M A PLANT MANAGER FOR UNICO.

AH, YES. ALEX!

I'M GOING TO A MANUFACTURERS' ASSOCIATION CONFERENCE BECAUSE MY PLANT HAS THE MOST EXPERIENCE WITH INDUSTRIAL ROBOTS.

HAVE YOUR ROBOTS INCREASED PRODUCTIVITY AT YOUR PLANT?

YES-- A 36% IMPROVEMENT IN ONE AREA.

REALLY..? YOU'RE MAKING 36% MORE *MONEY* JUST FROM INSTALLING SOME ROBOTS?

WELL, NO-O-O.

ONLY *ONE* DEPARTMENT HAD A 36% IMPROVEMENT.

THEN YOU DIDN'T REALLY INCREASE PRODUCTIVITY.

I-I'M NOT SURE I UNDERSTAND.

ALEX, DID YOU SHIP EVEN *ONE* MORE PRODUCT PER DAY AS A RESULT OF INSTALLING THE ROBOTS?

I-I'D HAVE TO CHECK.

DID YOU *FIRE* ANYBODY?

BECAUSE OF THE ROBOTS? NO. WE SHIFTED WORKERS AROUND.

DID YOUR INVENTORIES GO DOWN?

IF YOUR INVENTORIES HAVEN'T GONE DOWN...AND YOUR EMPLOYEE EXPENSE IS UNCHANGED...AND YOUR COMPANY *ISN'T* SELLING MORE PRODUCT--

--THEN THOSE ROBOTS HAVEN'T INCREASED YOUR PRODUCTIVITY.

AGAIN, I'D HAVE TO CHECK.

BUT MY *EFFICIENCIES* WENT UP AND MY *COSTS* WENT DOWN!

DID THEY?

SURE THEY DID!

YOUR INVENTORIES ARE GOING THROUGH THE ROOF, ARE THEY NOT?

HOW DOES HE KNOW?

SOME PLACES, YES, ARE HIGH.

AND EVERYTHING IS ALWAYS LATE?

WAIT A MINUTE--! HOW DO YOU *KNOW* THESE THINGS?

JUST A HUNCH.

I'M A SCIENTIST, ALEX...DOING WORK IN THE *SCIENCE OF ORGANIZATIONS*-- MANUFACTURING ORGANIZATIONS.

I SEE THESE SYMPTOMS IN A LOT OF MANUFACTURING PLANTS.

BUT NOW I'VE GOT TO CATCH MY FLIGHT.

15

I'M CURIOUS. WHAT MADE YOU SUSPECT SOMETHING MIGHT BE WRONG WITH MY PLANT?

YOU TOLD ME YOURSELF.

NO, I DIDN'T.

ALEX, IT'S CLEAR FROM YOUR OWN WORDS, YOU'RE RUNNING A VERY INEFFICIENT PLANT.

NOT ACCORDING TO MEASUREMENTS. ARE YOU SAYING MY PEOPLE ARE LYING TO ME?

IT'S UNLIKELY YOUR PEOPLE ARE. BUT YOUR MEASUREMENTS *DEFINITELY* ARE.

YEAH, SOMETIMES WE *MASSAGE* THE NUMBERS, BUT--

YOU'RE MISSING THE POINT. YOU THINK YOU'RE RUNNING AN EFFICIENT PLANT... BUT YOUR THINKING IS WRONG.

BUT... BUT IT'S THE SAME AS OTHER MANAGERS.

EXACTLY. ALEX, YOU'VE ACCEPTED SO MANY THINGS WITHOUT QUESTION THAT YOU'RE NOT REALLY THINKING AT ALL.

YES, I AM--THAT'S PART OF MY JOB!

ALEX, TELL ME AGAIN WHY YOU BELIEVE YOUR ROBOTS ARE SUCH A GREAT IMPROVEMENT.

BECAUSE THEY INCREASED *PRODUCTIVITY*.

AND WHAT IS PRODUCTIVITY?

IT MEANS THAT I'M ACCOMPLISHING SOMETHING.

EXACTLY! BUT IN TERMS OF WHAT?

IN TERMS OF GOALS.

YOU'RE JUST PLAYING A LOT OF *GAMES* WITH NUMBERS AND WORDS.

ROGO'S REVERIE OVER, HE IS FRUSTRATED BY PEACH'S PRESENTATION.

IT'S TEN O'CLOCK. LET'S TAKE A *BREAK*. BE BACK IN FIFTEEN MINUTES.

WHAT THE HELL AM I DOING HERE? MY WORLD'S BEEN TURNED UPSIDE DOWN. I DON'T EVEN KNOW WHAT PRODUCTIVITY IS NOW.

NONE OF US HAS ASKED THE BASIC QUESTION, "WHAT'S THE REAL GOAL?" SO HOW CAN THIS MEETING BE ANYTHING EXCEPT A TOTAL WASTE?

PEACH IS GOING TO BE MAD, BUT I'M GOING BACK TO THE PLANT.

REALIZING THAT HE NEEDS TO THINK THINGS THROUGH, ROGO PICKS UP SOME BEER AND PIZZA AND HEADS TO A SCENIC SITE.

20

ALEX ROGO ARRIVES AT THE PLANT AT 4:30 P.M. BUT INSTEAD OF USING THE MAIN ENTRANCE, TO AVOID HIS PEOPLE WAITING FOR HIM HE OPTS FOR THE SIDE DOOR...

HEADS UP! IT'S THE *BOSS*. BACK TO WORK.

WHAT THE--? DAMMIT!

THEY KNOW THE PLANT'S IN TROUBLE! YOU'D THINK THEY'D BE WORKING HARDER TO SAVE IT.

LIKE THOSE GUYS! THEY'RE WORKING! BUT...

...ARE THEY PRODUCTIVE?

WE'VE GOT LOTS OF PRODUCTION GOAL MEASUREMENTS. BUT DO THEY REALLY MAKE US MONEY, OR ARE THEY JUST ACCOUNTING GAMES?

LESS THAN A MINUTE AFTER ALEX ARRIVES AT HIS OFFICE, *LOU*, HIS PLANT COMPTROLLER, ENTERS.

THOSE ARE THE KIND I LIKE.

UPDATES ON FIGURES-- I EMAILED HIM MOST OF IT. THE REST HE'LL HAVE TOMORROW.

WHAT'D PEACH WANT, LOU?

OKAY, JUST LET ME SEE IT FIRST. LOU...I'VE GOT A SIMPLE, FUNDAMENTAL QUESTION FOR YOU.

WOULD YOU SAY THE *GOAL* OF THIS COMPANY IS TO MAKE MONEY?

IS THIS A TRICK QUESTION? *OF COURSE* IT'S TO MAKE MONEY!

SO HOW DO WE KNOW IF WE'RE MAKING MONEY?

LOU PROCEEDS TO LIST THE MEASUREMENTS: TOTAL SALES, MARKET SHARE...

HOW ABOUT *NET* PROFIT?

YOU NEED SOMETHING MORE THAN AN ABSOLUTE MEASUREMENT LIKE NET PROFIT. YOU ALSO NEED *ROI*-- RETURN ON INVESTMENTS-- THE COMPARISON OF *MONEY MADE* RELATIVE TO *MONEY INVESTED*.

BUT, IT'S POSSIBLE TO SHOW NET PROFIT *AND A GOOD ROI* AND STILL GO BANKRUPT. BAD CASH FLOW IS USUALLY THE CULPRIT.

STAY IN THE BLACK ON CASH FLOW AND YOU'RE OKAY. GO IN THE RED, AND YOU'RE DEAD...

...IT'S HAPPENING TO US RIGHT HERE, ISN'T IT?

SOMETIME LATER...

I'VE GOT TO SHOW YOU SOMETHING, DADDY!

WHAT'S THAT, MIZ MUFFET?

Gino's

Coca Cola

THIS. MY REPORT CARD.

YOU GOT ALL *A's!* THAT'S *TERRIFIC!* I'M REALLY PROUD OF YOU.

REPORT CARD

UH-OH. NINE O'CLOCK! C'MON GUYS. BEDTIME.

AWWWW!

BUT I GOT *STRAIGHT A'S!*

AND TO KEEP GETTING THOSE A'S YOU NEED YOUR SLEEP!

MAYBE JONAH'S NUMBER IS SOMEWHERE IN MY COLLEGE PAPERS AT MOM'S.

I HAVEN'T SEEN MOM IN A LONG TIME...

LOOKS LIKE AL HAD A HARD DAY, TOO.

THE DAY TURNS OUT EXACTLY AS EXPECTED, WITH PEACH RIPPING INTO HIM, AND A LONG-DELAYED MEETING THAT TAKES FOREVER. FINALLY, AT THE END OF THE DAY...

HI, MOM.

OH, MY GOD. WHO'S *DEAD?*

NOBODY.

IT'S JULIE. DID SHE LEAVE YOU?

NOT YET. I JUST MISS YOU.

COME IN-- COME IN, BEFORE YOU CATCH YOUR *DEATH OF COLD!*

YOU LIVE HERE IN TOWN, BUT I NEVER SEE YOU. TOO IMPORTANT NOW FOR YOUR OLD MOTHER?

NO. I'VE JUST BEEN BUSY. LISTEN, MOM, ANY IDEA WHERE MY OLD COLLEGE NOTES MIGHT BE?

PROBABLY IN THE ATTIC WITH YOUR OTHER STUFF....

...OR IN THE BASEMENT... OR YOUR OLD ROOM...

ALEX FINDS JONAH'S OLD PHONE NUMBER IN HIS NOTES.

26

YES, BUT THEIR DEFINITIONS ARE NOT. YOU'LL WANT TO WRITE THEM DOWN.

THROUGHPUT IS THE RATE AT WHICH THE SYSTEM GENERATES MONEY THROUGH SALES.

WOULDN'T IT BE MORE CORRECT TO SAY *PRODUCTION?*

NO. IF YOU PRODUCE SOMETHING. BUT DON'T SELL IT, IT'S *NOT* THROUGHPUT.

ALEX, THESE DEFINITIONS SOUND SIMPLE, BUT THEY ARE WORDED VERY *PRECISELY.*

A MEASUREMENT NOT CLEARLY DEFINED IS WORSE THAN USELESS.

UNDERSTOOD. GO ON.

INVENTORY IS ALL THE MONEY THAT THE SYSTEM HAS INVESTED IN PURCHASING THINGS IT INTENDS TO SELL.

OPERATIONAL EXPENSE IS ALL THE MONEY THE SYSTEM SPENDS IN ORDER TO TURN INVENTORY INTO THROUGHPUT.

ACCORDING TO THIS, THEN, LABOR INVESTED IN INVENTORY IS AN OPERATIONAL EXPENSE.

BUT SHOULDN'T IT BE A PART OF INVENTORY?

IT MIGHT BE, BUT IT DOESN'T HAVE TO BE. IT'S BETTER NOT TO TAKE THE VALUE ADDED INTO ACCOUNT. IT ELIMINATES THE CONFUSION OVER WHETHER A DOLLAR SPENT IS AN INVESTMENT OR AN EXPENSE.

ALEX, I HAVE TO GO. JUST REMEMBER WE ARE ALWAYS TALKING ABOUT THE ORGANIZATION AS A WHOLE--NOT ABOUT THE MANUFACTURING DEPARTMENT OR ANY OTHER SINGLE DEPARTMENT. WE ARE NOT CONCERNED WITH LOCAL OPTIMUMS.

OKAY. BUT HOW DO I RELATE THESE MEASUREMENTS TO MY PLANT? HOW DO I USE THEM TO EXPRESS THE GOAL OF MAKING MONEY?

ALEX GIVES JONAH THE DIRECT LINE TO HIS OFFICE.

BEFORE HE CAN THANK HIM, JONAH HAS HUNG UP.

DON'T JUST MISS ME WHEN YOU NEED SOMETHING.

BYE, MOM.

I LOVE YOU.

LOU MAKES A CALL, AND A FEW MINUTES LATER INVENTORY CONTROL MANAGER, STACEY POTAZENIK, ARRIVES. ALEX ASKS HER ABOUT WORK-IN-PROGRESS ON THOSE PARTS PASSING THROUGH THE ROBOT AREAS.

WHEN THE REPORTS CAME IN, WE FOUND THE ROBOTS AVERAGED *THIRTY PERCENT* EFFICIENCY. NOBODY WOULD STAND FOR THAT, SO ORDERS WENT OUT TO INCREASE ROBOT OUTPUT, THUS THEIR EFFICIENCIES. AND INVENTORY.

DO YOU WANT EXACT NUMBERS?

TRENDS WILL DO.

I CAN TELL YOU WITHOUT LOOKING THAT INVENTORIES WENT *UP* SINCE THIRD QUARTER LAST YEAR.

AND I'M *SURE* THAT ALL THIS HAPPENED BEFORE YOU BECAME PLANT MANAGER.

I DON'T THINK YOU WERE HERE YET AT THAT TIME, ALEX.

THE IMPORTANT THING WAS THAT EFFICIENCIES DID GO UP. NOBODY CAN FIND FAULT WITH THAT.

I'M NOT SO SURE, ANYMORE, LOU.

STACEY, WHY ARE WE GETTING THAT SURPLUS?

WHY AREN'T WE CONSUMING THOSE PARTS?

YOU NEED TO ASK BOB DONOVAN.

BOB, TALK TO US ABOUT OUR LOCAL CELEBRITIES, THE ROBOTS.

STACEY TELLS ME THEY'RE PRODUCING AN EXCESS OF PARTS, BUT THAT WE STILL CAN'T ASSEMBLE AND SHIP OUR ORDERS ON TIME.

IT ISN'T THAT WE CAN'T GET ENOUGH PARTS-- IT'S MORE THAT WE CAN'T SEEM TO GET *ALL* THE PARTS WE NEED FOR OUR ORDERS WHEN WE NEED THEM. SO, WE WAIT.

STACEY, WHY THIS *EXCESS* OF PARTS WE DON'T HAVE ORDERS FOR?

EVERYBODY TELLS ME WE'LL USE THEM EVENTUALLY. WE BUILD INVENTORY.

IF THE EFFICIENCIES DON'T HOLD UP, THERE'S HELL TO PAY. *THAT'S* WHAT'S BEEN HAPPENING FOR THE BETTER PART OF A YEAR.

SO, THE BOTTOM LINE IS THIS: TO GIVE THE ROBOTS MORE TO DO, WE RELEASED MORE MATERIALS.

WHICH, IN TURN, INCREASED INVENTORIES.

WHICH HAS INCREASED OUR COSTS.

BUT THE COST OF EACH *PART* WENT DOWN.

WAREHOUSES.

FINISHED GOODS.

FOR WHAT?

WOULD UNICO STAY IN BUSINESS IF ALL IT DID WAS MANUFACTURE PRODUCTS TO FILL THOSE WAREHOUSES?

OKAY. SO WE GOT TO SELL THE STUFF TO MAKE MONEY.

INTERESTING... EACH DEFINITION CONTAINS THE WORD *MONEY*. ONE FOR INCOMING, ONE FOR MONEY STILL STUCK INSIDE, AND ONE FOR OUTGOING MONEY.

I DON'T SEE HOW HE'S TREATING VALUE ADDED TO MATERIALS BY DIRECT LABOR.

JONAH SAID IT'S BETTER IF VALUE ADDED ISN'T TAKEN INTO ACCOUNT-- IT ELIMINATES THE "CONFUSION" ABOUT WHAT'S AN INVESTMENT AND WHAT'S AN EXPENSE.

PERHAPS BECAUSE WE "BUY" TIME FROM OUR EMPLOYEES BUT WE DON'T SELL THAT TIME TO A CUSTOMER-- UNLESS IT'S A *SERVICE*.

IF I UNDERSTAND IT CORRECTLY, ALL THIS IS JUST A DIFFERENT WAY OF DOING THE ACCOUNTING?

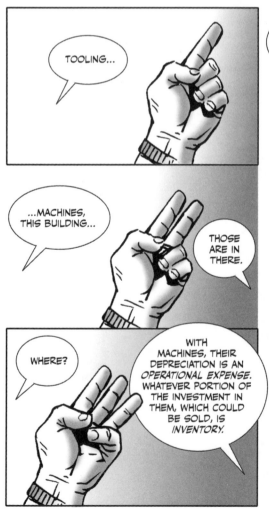

36

THE SUBJECT OF "KNOWLEDGE" INSPIRES A SPIRITED DEBATE ON HOW TO *CATEGORIZE* IT. THE GROUP DECIDES IT DEPENDS ON HOW THE "KNOWLEDGE" IS USED.

IF IT'S KNOWLEDGE THAT RESULTS IN A NEW MANUFACTURING PROCESS, IT'S AN *OPERATIONAL EXPENSE*. IF IT'S SOMETHING LIKE A PATENT OR A TECHNOLOGY LICENSE THAT HAS SALES POTENTIAL, THEN IT'S INVENTORY.

FINALLY, IF IT'S KNOWLEDGE THAT PERTAINS TO A *PRODUCT* UNICO WILL BUILD, IT'S TREATED LIKE A MACHINE-- A MONEY-MAKING INVESTMENT THAT WILL DEPRECIATE OVER TIME.

OKAY, THE PROBLEM WE HAVE IS THAT EVERYBODY-- INCLUDING ME UNTIL NOW-- HAS THOUGHT OUR NEW ROBOTS WERE A PRODUCTIVITY IMPROVEMENT.

TAP TAP TAP

BUT THIS SHOWS US THAT THE ROBOTS ARE NOT PRODUCTIVE IN TERMS OF THE *GOAL*. IN FACT, THE WAY WE'VE BEEN USING THEM MAKES THEM COUNTERPRODUCTIVE.

SO WE'VE GOT TO MAKE THE ROBOTS PRODUCTIVE IN TERMS OF THE GOAL.

WE'VE GOT TO DO *MORE* THAN THAT. HERE'S WHAT I TOLD LOU...

ROGO REVEALS PEACH'S ULTIMATUM: TURN THE PLANT AROUND IN THREE MONTHS OR IT'LL BE SHUT DOWN. HE TELLS THE TEAM THAT HE'S DETERMINED NOT TO GIVE UP.

AL, MAYBE YOU SHOULD TRY CALLING JONAH AGAIN.

GOOD IDEA.

ROOM 718, PLEASE.

JONAH? ALEX, HERE. I WAS WONDERING IF WE COULD MEET. THERE'S SOMETHING IMPORTANT I'D LIKE TO RUN BY YOU.

TOMORROW MORNING AT YOUR HOTEL? THAT WOULD BE FINE.

40

BUT OTHER KINDS OF INFORMATION ARE UNPREDICTABLE. FOR INSTANCE, HOW LONG THE WAITER WILL TAKE TO SERVE US OR HOW MANY EGGS THE KITCHEN WILL USE TODAY. BECAUSE THAT INFORMATION VARIES, THEY ARE SUBJECT TO *STATISTICAL FLUCTUATIONS*.

MOST OF THE FACTORS CRITICAL TO RUNNING YOUR PLANT SUCCESSFULLY CANNOT BE DETERMINED PRECISELY AHEAD OF TIME.

FRANKLY, I CAN'T SEE WHAT EITHER ONE OF THOSE TWO PHENOMENA HAVE TO DO WITH ANYTHING.

I'M NOT TALKING ABOUT EACH INDIVIDUALLY, BUT ABOUT THE EFFECT OF THEM *TOGETHER*.

WHICH IS WHAT I WANT YOU TO THINK ABOUT... BECAUSE I HAVE TO GO.

JONAH, I DON'T HAVE TIME FOR RIDDLES. I NEED *ANSWERS*.

ALEX, IF I SIMPLY *TOLD* YOU WHAT TO DO, ULTIMATELY, YOU'D FAIL.

TO MAKE THE RULES WORK, YOU HAVE TO GAIN UNDERSTANDING FOR YOURSELF. CALL ME WHEN YOU HAVE IT.

TAXI!!

50

51

THIS IS NOT GOOD.
I WANT THE KIDS TO ENJOY
THE WOODS, BUT EVERY TIME
SOMEONE GETS DISTRACTED,
HE FALLS BEHIND, AND
SO DOES EVERYONE
BEHIND HIM.

AND THERE
ARE OTHER
THINGS SLOWING
US DOWN.

55

THAT EVENING...

HERBIE WAS THE KEY TO FIXING THE PROBLEM WITH THE LINE. THE LINE... *THE ASSEMBLY LINE...*

JUST LIKE THE ASSEMBLY LINE AT THE PLANT, OUR HIKE TODAY WAS A SET OF DEPENDENT EVENTS--

THE WALKING SPEED OF THE KID IN FRONT OF YOU--IN COMBINATION WITH STATISTICAL FLUCTUATIONS--HOW FAST EACH KID WALKED FROM MINUTE TO MINUTE.

EVERYONE'S MAXIMUM SPEED WAS THE PACE OF THE BOY IN FRONT OF HIM, SAME AS HOW EACH PRODUCT ON A CONVEYOR BELT IS DEPENDENT ON HOW LONG IT TAKES FOR THE NEXT STAGE OF ASSEMBLY ON THE COMPONENT AHEAD OF IT.

WHILE THE BOYS' ABILITY TO *ACCELERATE* WAS RESTRICTED...

...THEIR ABILITY TO *SLOW DOWN* WAS NOT LIMITED. THE PROGRESS OF THE HIKE WAS AN ACCUMULATION OF SLOWNESS FLUCTUATIONS...

JUST LIKE ON THE ASSEMBLY LINE.

THE NEXT DAY THE GROUP IS ON THE TRAIL ONCE MORE. AND NOW THEY MAKE MUCH BETTER PROGRESS...

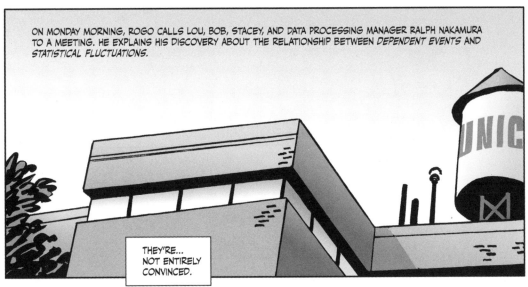

ON MONDAY MORNING, ROGO CALLS LOU, BOB, STACEY, AND DATA PROCESSING MANAGER RALPH NAKAMURA TO A MEETING. HE EXPLAINS HIS DISCOVERY ABOUT THE RELATIONSHIP BETWEEN *DEPENDENT EVENTS* AND *STATISTICAL FLUCTUATIONS.*

THEY'RE... NOT ENTIRELY CONVINCED.

ONLY REAL PROOF WILL CONVINCE THEM. THANKS TO HILTON SMYTH, THE SOON-TO-BE NEW DIVISION PRODUCTIVITY MANAGER, ROGO HAS ONE. SMYTH HAS DEMANDED 100 SUBASSEMBLIES FROM ROGO'S PLANT BY THE END OF THE DAY.

OUTPUT IS ONE HUNDRED PIECES BY FIVE P.M. HILTON WON'T ACCEPT A PARTIAL SHIPMENT.

THESE PIECES HAVE TO GO THROUGH TWO WORK STATIONS, PETE SCHNELL'S FABRICATING DEPARTMENT AND THE ROBOT, BEFORE THEY ARE DONE.

AVERAGE HOURLY PRODUCTION BY PETE'S DEPARTMENT IS 25 PIECES. SOMETIMES THERE'LL BE A FEW MORE, SOMETIMES A FEW LESS. THAT'S A STATISTICAL FLUCTUATION.

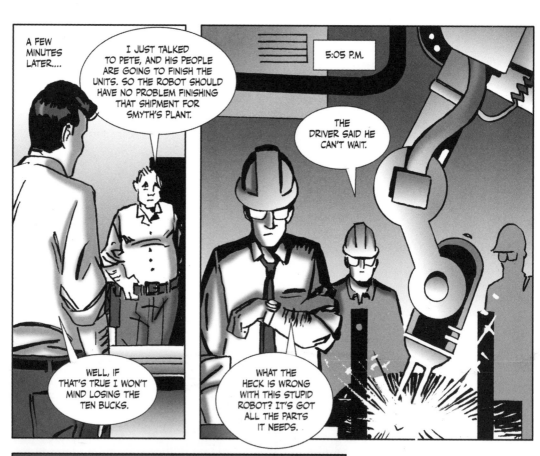

IN THE CONFERENCE CALL JONAH ONLY HAS A FEW MINUTES. ROGO QUICKLY SUMMARIZES HIS LESSON LEARNED ON THE HIKE AND YESTERDAY'S EXPERIMENT. HE SAYS SOME RESOURCES, PARTICULARLY AT THE PRODUCTION LINE'S END, WILL NEED MORE CAPACITY THAN THOSE AT THE BEGINNING.

AM I RIGHT, JONAH?

YOU'RE ON THE MONEY, ALEX.

NOW YOU NEED TO DISTINGUISH BETWEEN TWO TYPES OF *RESOURCES*. I CALL THEM BOTTLENECK AND NON-BOTTLENECK RESOURCES.

A BOTTLENECK IS ANY RESOURCE WHOSE *CAPACITY* IS EQUAL TO OR LESS THAN THE *DEMAND* PLACED UPON IT.

AND A NON-BOTTLENECK IS ANY RESOURCE WHOSE CAPACITY IS *GREATER* THAN THE DEMAND PLACED ON IT.

RALPH NAKAMURA AND HIS DEPARTMENT BEGIN CRUNCHING DATA IN ORDER TO CALCULATE DEMAND. THEIR WORK QUICKLY EVOLVES INTO A "FOREST-AND-TREES" PROCESS, WITH PLENTY OF DEAD ENDS.

TWO HOURS ARE WASTED DETERMINING DEMAND FOR *MILLING MACHINES* LISTED ON INVENTORY...

...THAT WERE SOLD A YEAR AGO.

THE MORE DATA THEY GATHER AND ASSESS, THE MORE THEY DISCOVER IT'S OFTEN INCOMPLETE, OR INACCURATE.

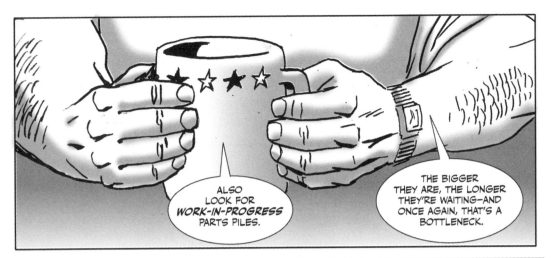

ALSO LOOK FOR *WORK-IN-PROGRESS* PARTS PILES.

THE BIGGER THEY ARE, THE LONGER THEY'RE WAITING—AND ONCE AGAIN, THAT'S A BOTTLENECK.

LATER...

HERE'S OUR FIRST BOTTLENECK, THE *NCX-10,* WITH A BACKLOG OF *MONTHS,* ACCORDING TO RALPH AND STACEY.

BUT IT'S SUPPOSED TO BE ONE OF OUR MOST *EFFICIENT* MACHINES.

IT IS. IT DOES WHAT THREE MACHINES USED TO DO, AND SAVES FOUR MINUTES FROM UNIT PRODUCTION TIME. BUT THERE'S A TRADE-OFF.

BOB EXPLAINS THAT THOUGH *PER* UNIT THE OLD THREE-MACHINE SYSTEM WAS SLOWER BECAUSE MORE MACHINES WERE INVOLVED, THE OVERALL OUTPUT WAS HIGHER. ALSO NCX-10 OPERATOR TRAINING AND TURNOVER PROVED A CHRONIC PROBLEM, SLOWING ITS OUTPUT FURTHER.

NCX-1

BOB THEN TAKES ROGO TO BOTTLENECK #2, THE HEAT-TREAT DEPARTMENT. HERE, BOB EXPLAINS THE PROBLEM IS DIFFERENT. PARTS HAVE DIFFERENT REQUIREMENTS IN TEMPERATURE AND HEATING DURATIONS, CAUSING THE FURNACES TO OFTEN RUN AT HALF-CAPACITY.

TELL ME SOMETHING, BOB.

IF WE FILLED THE FURNACE EVERY TIME, WOULD WE HAVE ENOUGH CAPACITY TO MEET DEMAND?

I DON'T KNOW. WE'VE NEVER DONE IT THAT WAY BEFORE.

OKAY, WE IDENTIFIED OUR BOTTLENECKS--CLEARLY, WE CAN'T REARRANGE PRODUCTION TO PUT THEM AT THE BEGINNING OF THE PROCESS.

WE'VE HIT A WALL. CAN WE CALL JONAH AGAIN?

QUICKLY ROGO EXPLAINS THEIR SITUATION.

IT'S A SHORT CALL.

I'M PICKING JONAH UP AT THE AIRPORT. HE'LL BE HERE TOMORROW.

THE NEXT MORNING...

BEARINGTON REGIONAL AIRPORT

JONAH, THANKS FOR COMING!

ROGO BRIEFS JONAH DURING THE DRIVE TO THE PLANT. AFTER INTRODUCING HIM TO HIS MANAGERS, THEY WALK ONTO THE SHOP FLOOR.

THE NCX-10 IS ONE OF OUR BOTTLENECKS.

WHY'S IT NOT WORKING?

THE SET-UP PEOPLE ARE ON BREAK--UNION RULES, EVERY FOUR HOURS, A HALF-HOUR BREAK.

THEY'LL BE BACK IN 20 MINUTES.

ON ANY NON-BOTTLENECK MACHINE HERE, NO PROBLEM. BUT ON A BOTTLENECK? IT'S A REAL PROBLEM.

WHAT'S THE PRODUCTION HOURS FOR IT?

AROUND 585 HOURS A MONTH.

A BOTTLENECK DOWNTIME HOUR--OR EVEN HALF-HOUR--IS UNRECOVERABLE.

YOUR PLANT'S **OVERALL THROUGHPUT** IS LOWER BY WHATEVER AMOUNT THIS BOTTLENECK COULD HAVE PRODUCED IN THAT TIME, MAKING THIS AN ENORMOUSLY EXPENSIVE LUNCH BREAK. .

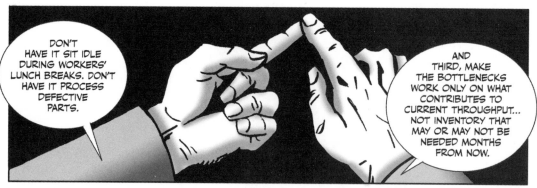

BOB REARRANGES THE Q.C. CHECKPOINT AT THE HEAT-TREAT FURNACE, AND MEETS WITH O'DONNELL, THE UNION REP, TO REVISE BREAK SCHEDULES FOR THE NCX-10.

RALPH CREATES A LIST THAT PRIORITIZES THE OVERDUE ORDERS, PUTTING THE MOST RECENT ORDERS AT THE BOTTOM. ALL PRODUCTION FOR INVENTORY HAS BEEN PUT ON HOLD. THE TOTAL COMES TO 67 BACKLOGGED ORDERS. THE WORST IS 58 DAYS OVERDUE,

THREE ARE JUST ONE DAY LATE, WITH THE REST SCATTERED IN BETWEEN.

THEN HE AND STACEY WORK LATE INTO THE NIGHT SORTING ALL THE BILLS OF LADING AND INVENTORY RECORDS TO FIND WHERE THINGS ARE AND WHAT'S NEEDED FOR FINISHING.

RALPH AND STACEY FIND ABOUT 90 PERCENT OF THE OVERDUES ARE WAITING IN FINAL ASSEMBLY FOR PARTS FLOWING THROUGH ONE OR BOTH BOTTLENECKS.

THEY THEN MAKE A LIST IDENTIFYING PARTS AND *PROCESSING SEQUENCE* FOR BOTH HEAT-TREAT AND NCX-10 MACHINES.

HEAT TREAT

NCX-10

PRODUCTION LINE

THE NEXT MORNING, AFTER CALLING IN *TED SPENCER* AND *MARIO DEMONTE*-- THE HEAT-TREAT FURNACE AND NCX-10 SUPERVISORS--RALPH AND STACEY PRESENT THEIR FINDINGS.

YOU GUYS HAVE DONE A SUPER JOB.

TED, MARIO, HAVE YOUR FOREMEN START AT THE *TOP* OF THIS LIST AND WORK THEIR WAY DOWN.

I THINK WE CAN HANDLE THAT.

YOU JUST WANT US TO DO WHAT'S ON THIS LIST?

YEP. IF THE EXPEDITERS GIVE YOU CRAP, TELL THEM TO SEE ME.

ROGO THEN MEETS WITH *MIKE O'DONNELL* ABOUT THE BREAK RESCHEDULING, AND INFORMS THE UNION REPRESENTATIVE FOR THE FIRST TIME ABOUT THE PLANT'S AT-RISK STATUS.

LATER THAT MORNING...

WHAT THE *HELL?*

WHERE'S DONOVAN? HE'D BETTER HAVE A GOOD REASON... *AH!* THERE HE IS.

NCX-10

TO GET EVERYONE ON BOARD, AT THE BEGINNING OF THE NEXT SHIFT ROGO HOLDS A FIFTEEN-MINUTE MEETING TO INFORM WORKERS OF THE PRODUCTION POLICY CHANGE THAT PRIORITIZES WORK TO KEEP THE TWO BOTTLENECKS SUPPLIED WITH THE RIGHT PARTS.

DONOVAN THEN EXPLAINS THAT ALL WORK-IN-PROGRESS WILL HAVE *COLOR-CODED* TAGS. RED-TAGGED PARTS HAVE PRIORITY. ALL OTHERS WILL HAVE GREEN TAGS.

THE GREEN-TAGGED PARTS ARE WORKED ON ONLY IF THERE ARE NO RED-TAGGED PARTS IN THE QUEUE.

WHEN *RED-TAGGED* PARTS ARRIVE, STOP THE *GREEN-TAGGED* JOB AS SOON AS YOU CAN AND THEN WORK ON THE RED-TAGGED PARTS.

LATER THAT AFTERNOON...

AL, THIS IS O'DONNELL. THE UNION'S APPROVED YOUR NEW LUNCH BREAK POLICY.

THANKS, MIKE. APPRECIATE IT.

WITH EVERYONE ON BOARD, THE *NCX-10* AND *HEAT-TREAT* FURNACE BOTTLENECKS ARE NOT ONLY GETTING PARTS ON TIME, THE PILES OF PARTS WAITING FOR THEM ARE GETTING BIGGER.

AND QUALITY CONTROL INSPECTIONS REJECTING DEFECTIVE PARTS BEFORE REACHING THE NCX-10 AND HEAT-TREAT FURNACES RESULT IN A NET GAIN OF FIVE AND SEVEN PERCENT RESPECTIVELY.

REJECTED

THE CHANGE IN LUNCH AND COFFEE BREAK SCHEDULES ALSO BOOSTS THROUGHPUT. THE RESULT IS THAT ONE WEEK LATER...

WELL, ALEX, OUR TWELVE MOST OVERDUE ORDERS HAVE *SHIPPED!*

IT'S A STEP IN THE RIGHT DIRECTION, BUT WE HAVE TO ACCELERATE THE PROCESS.

BOB, HOW ARE WE COMING WITH JONAH'S OTHER SUGGESTIONS?

WE'RE LOOKING INTO THEM.

I WANT RECOMMENDATIONS BY WEDNESDAY.

OKAY.

SO, IT'S NOT JUST THE FURNACE, THE NCX-10 ALSO HAS SIGNIFICANT DOWNTIME DUE TO WORKERS BUSY ELSEWHERE?!

IN TALKING WITH BOB DONOVAN, ROGO DEMANDS RECOMENDATIONS FIRST THING THE FOLLOWING DAY.

THE NEXT MORNING, HE GETS THEM.

THEY INCLUDE ROUND-THE-CLOCK *DEDICATED TEAMS* AT BOTH MACHINES, ONE-SHIFT OPERATION OF THE NCX-10 SUPPLEMENTAL TRIO OF OBSOLETE MACHINES, AND USING AN OUTSIDE VENDOR FOR SOME HEAT-TREAT ORDERS.

LOU, WHAT'S YOUR TAKE?

KNOWING WHAT WE KNOW NOW, IT'S PERFECTLY LEGITIMATE FOR US TO ASSIGN ADDITIONAL PEOPLE TO THE BOTTLENECKS IF IT WILL INCREASE OUR THROUGHPUT.

GOOD. LET'S *DO* IT. AND, BOB, MAKE SURE ONLY OUR *BEST PEOPLE* WORK THE BOTTLENECKS.

TO KEEP UP MORALE, ESPECIALLY WITH THE TWO BOTTLENECK TEAMS, ROGO MAKES A POINT OF VISITING AND TALKING TO THEM. HIS VISIT WITH THIRD-SHIFT FOREMAN MIKE HALEY PROVES EYE-OPENING.

MIKE, WHAT ARE THOSE GUYS DOING?

GETTING READY FOR WHEN WE HAVE TO RELOAD A FURNACE, MR. ROGO.

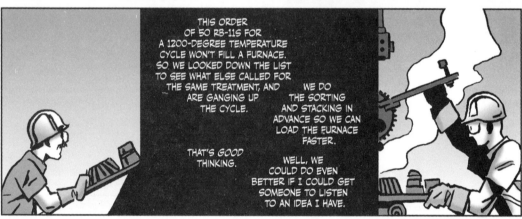

THIS ORDER OF 50 RB-11S FOR A 1200-DEGREE TEMPERATURE CYCLE WON'T FILL A FURNACE. SO, WE LOOKED DOWN THE LIST TO SEE WHAT ELSE CALLED FOR THE SAME TREATMENT, AND ARE GANGING UP THE CYCLE.

WE DO THE SORTING AND STACKING IN ADVANCE SO WE CAN LOAD THE FURNACE FASTER.

THAT'S *GOOD* THINKING.

WELL, WE COULD DO EVEN BETTER IF I COULD GET SOMEONE TO LISTEN TO AN IDEA I HAVE.

TELL ME.

IF ENGINEERING COULD TAKE SOME STEEL PLATES AND MAKE *INTERCHANGEABLE LOADING TABLES*, THEY COULD SAVE A COUPLE OF HOURS LOADING AND UNLOADING PARTS EACH DAY, FURTHER BOOSTING WEEKLY OUTPUT.

I *LIKE* IT. I'LL HAVE BOB DONOVAN TALK TO YOU TO FORMALIZE IT.

LATER THAT MORNING...

HI, BOB. GET MY NOTE ON HALEY?

IT'S BEING TAKEN CARE OF.

GOOD. LET'S REMEMBER HIM WHEN OUR PAY FREEZE IS LIFTED.

MORE GOOD NEWS. REMEMBER WHEN JONAH ASKED US ABOUT PARTS NEEDING HEAT-TREAT?

WELL, I DISCOVERED THAT IN THREE CASES, *WE*-- NOT ENGINEERING-- MADE THE SPECIFICATION.

WHAT?

DONOVAN EXPLAINS THAT FIVE YEARS AGO, TO IMPROVE EFFICIENCIES, SOME HOTSHOTS SPED UP CUTTING-TOOL PROCESSING, RESULTING IN THINNER, MORE BRITTLE PARTS THAT NEEDED HEAT-TREATING TO COUNTERACT THE MILLING.

GOING BACK TO THE OLDER, SLOWER METHOD--WHICH WE CAN DO SINCE WE MADE THE RULE, NOT ENGINEERING--REDUCES 20 PERCENT OF THE HEAT-TREAT LOAD.

BY *REDUCING* EFFICIENCY, WE *INCREASE* PRODUCTION. THEY'D NEVER BELIEVE IT ON THE FIFTEENTH FLOOR!

BUT THE CELEBRATION PROVES SHORT-LIVED.

MONDAY MORNING...

YOU'RE NOT GOING TO LIKE THIS, ALEX. BUT THE BOTTLENECKS HAVE *SPREAD*.

WHAT? HOW?

TAKE A LOOK AT THIS: LAST WEEK'S ORDER FOR 200 DBD-50'S. OUT OF 172 DIFFERENT PARTS, WE WERE MISSING 17. OF THAT 17, ONLY *ONE* WAS RED TAGGED.

IS THERE A MATERIALS SHORTAGE ON THOSE GREEN-TAGGED PARTS, OR MAYBE A VENDOR PROBLEM?

NO. THE PROBLEM IS DEFINITELY *INTERNAL*. MAYBE WITH THE INCREASE IN THROUGHPUT, WE'VE RUN OUT OF CAPACITY ELSEWHERE.

FIND OUT WHICH PARTS, HOW MANY, PRODUCTS AFFECTED-- EVERYTHING YOU CAN. JONAH WILL BE HERE TOMORROW AND WE CAN DISCUSS THIS WITH HIM.

I'M ON IT.

ARRIVALS

THE NEXT MORNING...

HELLO, JONAH. PERFECT TIMING. MY PEOPLE ARE WAITING WITH QUESTIONS FOR YOU.

I SPENT LAST NIGHT ON THIS. THE PROBLEM COVERS THIRTY PARTS.

THEY'RE RELEASED ACCORDING TO SCHEDULE, BUT NOT REACHING FINAL ASSEMBLY-- STUCK IN FRONT OF OUR *NEW* BOTTLENECK.

WAIT A MINUTE. HOW DO YOU KNOW IT'S REALLY A BOTTLENECK?

WELL, SINCE THE PARTS ARE HELD UP--

BEFORE WE JUMP TO CONCLUSIONS, LET'S GO INTO THE PLANT AND SEE WHAT'S HAPPENING.

THEY SEE WHAT STACEY IS TALKING ABOUT AT ONE OF THE MILLING MACHINE CENTERS-- *BACKED UP PARTS* ALL BEARING GREEN TAGS.

YEAH, THEY'VE BEEN SITTIN' HERE FOR ABOUT TWO, THREE WEEKS OR MORE.

WE'VE BEEN DOIN' ALL THESE RED-TAG PARTS FIRST, LIKE YOU SAID. WE GET TO THE GREEN ONES WHEN WE CAN, BUT THERE'S ONLY SO MANY HOURS IN THE DAY.

I GUESS OUR ONLY SOLUTION NOW IS TO *EXPEDITE!*

NO, ACTUALLY, THAT IS NOT THE SOLUTION. DO THAT, AND IT'LL ONLY GET WORSE.

LET'S GO LOOK AT THE BOTTLENECKS, BECAUSE THERE IS ANOTHER ASPECT TO THE PROBLEM.

NINETY PERCENT IS A MORE ACCEPTABLE NUMBER.

WHY? NUMBERS NOT BASED ON THE *CONSTRAINTS* OF THE SYSTEM ARE MEANINGLESS.

SO MAKING AN EMPLOYEE WORK AND PROFITING FROM THAT WORK ARE TWO *DIFFERENT* THINGS.

YES, PAY ATTENTION: ACTIVATING A RESOURCE AND UTILIZING A RESOURCE ARE NOT SYNONYMOUS.

JONAH EXPLAINS THAT "UTILIZING" A RESOURCE MEANS MAKING USE OF IT IN A WAY THAT MOVES THE SYSTEM TOWARD THE GOAL. "ACTIVATING" A RESOURCE IS LIKE PRESSING THE "ON" SWITCH OF A MACHINE. IT RUNS REGARDLESS OF OVERALL BENEFIT TO THE SYSTEM. SO RUNNING A NON-BOTTLENECK MACHINE TO ITS MAXIMUM IS AN ACT OF MAXIMUM STUPIDITY.

THIS HAS INCREASED THE MILLING MACHINES' LOAD, PUSHING IT OVER ITS CAPACITY, CAUSING GREEN-TAGGED PARTS TO PILE UP.

IN ADDITION TO EXCESS INVENTORY AT THE NCX-10 AND HEAT-TREAT, THE BOTTLENECK PARTS VOLUME CLOGS WORKFLOW AT ANOTHER STATION, PREVENTING NON-BOTTLENECK PARTS FROM REACHING ASSEMBLY.

SO, WHAT SHOULD WE DO TO *CORRECT* THE PROBLEM?

THE SOLUTION IS FAIRLY SIMPLE.

JONAH EXPLAINS THAT ONCE RALPH DETERMINES A BOTTLENECK-BASED, RED-TAG MATERIALS RELEASE SCHEDULE, HE CAN THEN DETERMINE A *FINAL ASSEMBLY SCHEDULE.* UPON KNOWING FINAL ASSEMBLY ARRIVAL TIME OF BOTTLENECK PARTS, HE CAN CALCULATE BACKWARDS AND SCHEDULE RELEASE DATES OF RELEVANT NON-BOTTLENECK MATERIALS.

FASCINATING... THIS *DOES* SOUND A LOT LIKE THE PROBLEM YOUR FATHER HAS AT THE PLANT. DAVID, SHARON, WOULD YOU LIKE TO HELP US SOLVE IT?

SURE!

OKAY. HERE'S THE PROBLEM--LET'S GO BACK TO HERBIE AND THE SCOUTS. HERBIE IS IN THE MIDDLE OF THE LINE, AND NOW HE HAS TO STAY IN THE MIDDLE-- KIDS BEHIND HIM CAN'T GO AROUND HIM.

THE PROBLEM IS THAT EVERYONE IN THE LINE HAS TO STAY THE SAME DISTANCE APART. THEY CAN'T BUNCH UP OR SPREAD OUT; THEY HAVE TO MOVE AT THE SAME PACE. HOW DO WE MAKE SURE THAT HAPPENS?

THINK YOU CAN SOLVE THE PROBLEM BEFORE DESSERT?

I DON'T KNOW ABOUT DAVID, BUT I BET *I CAN!*

YOU KIDS CAN GO IN THE OTHER ROOM AND WORK ON IT WHILE YOUR FATHER AND I CLEAR THE TABLE.

A FEW MINUTES LATER...

I GOT IT, MR. JONAH!

ME TOO! AND, MINE'S BETTER!

WHAT'S YOUR IDEA, SHARON?

A DRUMMER! LIKE IN A PARADE. EVERYONE IN THE BAND MARCHES IN STEP. AND HERBIE BEATS THE DRUM.

THAT'S A VERY GOOD IDEA, SHARON.

SO, DAVID, WHAT'S YOUR SOLUTION?

TIE ROPES TO EVERYONE, LIKE MOUNTAIN CLIMBERS. THAT WAY NO ONE GETS LEFT BEHIND OR PULLS AWAY FROM THE OTHERS.

THE ONLY WAY ANYONE CAN GO FASTER IS IF *EVERYONE* GOES FASTER.

THAT'S ANOTHER GOOD IDEA. CONGRATULATIONS, YOU *TWO!* OF COURSE, WE CAN'T ACTUALLY USE A ROPE OR A DRUM AT THE PLANT...

...AND SOMETIMES WE HAVE MORE THAN ONE "HERBIE" TO DEAL WITH.

BUT AS YOU SUGGESTED, HERBIE SHOULD BE THE DRUMMER FOR ALL OTHER PRODUCTION UNITS IN THE PLANT. HE SHOULD BE THE ONE SETTING THE PACE.

IF WE MAKE HERBIE GO FASTER OR SLOWER, HE WILL BEAT THE DRUM AND ALL OTHER WORKSTATIONS WILL FOLLOW.

WE WANT THE BOTTLENECK TO WORK AS FAST AS POSSIBLE, SO WE BETTER MAKE SURE HE ALWAYS HAS SOMETHING TO WORK ON.

PRECISELY. HERBIE NEEDS A BUFFER IN FRONT OF HIM-- ENOUGH WORK TO MAKE SURE HE NEVER STARVES.

AND DAVY'S ROPE IS ALSO IMPORTANT--ALL OTHER PRODUCTION UNITS ARE TIED TO HERBIE.

THE ROPE IS TIED ALL THE WAY TO THE BEGINNING, TELLING US WHEN TO RELEASE MORE RAW MATERIALS TO THE FLOOR.

THE ROPE IS TIED ALL THE WAY TO THE END ALLOWING US TO PREDICT WHEN PARTS WILL REACH FINAL ASSEMBLY AND WHAT DUE DATES TO PROMISE.

SO THE SOLUTION IS A COMBINATION OF THE DRUM AND THE ROPE WITH A BUFFER BETWEEN THEM. THE BUFFER DETERMINES HOW LOOSE THE ROPE IS.

WE DON'T WANT THE ROPE TO BE TOO TIGHT IN FRONT OF HERBIE BECAUSE EVERY DISTURBANCE WILL TEAR THE ROPE--WE WOULD LOSE THROUGHPUT FOR THE ENTIRE PLANT.

WOW. I CAN DEFINITELY SEE HOW THAT WILL HELP ADDRESS THE PROBLEM IN THE PLANT. *GOOD WORK, KIDS!*

AND BECAUSE DAVID AND SHARON CAME UP WITH THE *DRUM BUFFER ROPE* SYSTEM, HOW ABOUT WE'LL CALL IT *DBR* IN THEIR HONOR!

ALEX, JULIE, I WANT TO THANK YOU FOR A WONDERFUL EVENING. AND, I'D LIKE TO PROPOSE A TOAST...

...TO A GOAL ALL OF US HAVE, WHATEVER OUR DREAMS--TO SUCCESS.

CLINK!

TO SUCCESS!

THE NEXT MORNING...

AL, WHEN WE APPLY JONAH'S LATEST SUGGESTION, OUR EFFICIENCIES'LL GO DOWN. WE'LL HAVE A LOT OF IDLE WORKERS.

MIDDLE MANAGEMENT'S FLAWED STANDARDS GOT US IN THIS MESS. IF THERE'S IDLE TIME, LET'S KEEP IT OFF THE MONTHLY REPORTS TO HEADQUARTERS.

GOTCHA, BOSS.

UNICO HEADQUARTERS, ONE MONTH LATER...

IN CONCLUSION, THE BEARINGTON PLANT'S *INCREASE* IN OUTPUT AND REVENUE ENDED A SIX-MONTH STRING OF LOSSES FOR THE UNIWARE DIVISION. BUT WE STILL HAVE A LONG WAY TO GO.

THANK YOU, MISTER FROST.

NOW, ROGO, SINCE YOU'RE THE ONLY ONE SHOWING MAJOR IMPROVEMENT, YOU LEAD.

BEARINGTON

HAPPY TO.

ROGO'S REPORT IS IMPRESSIVE. HIS PLANT HAS SHOWN AN *ACROSS-THE-BOARD IMPROVEMENT*. INVENTORY LEVELS ARE FALLING AND CONTINUING TO DO SO. AFTER A TEMPORARY DIP, EFFICIENCIES ARE IMPROVING.

BEST OF ALL, THE BACKLOG OF OVERDUE ORDERS HAS BEEN ELIMINATED, AND THROUGHPUT IS UP.

GOOD JOB, AL.

AFTER THE MEETING, ROGO REQUESTS A MEETING WITH PEACH.

SO, WHEN ARE YOU GOING TO LET US OFF THE HOOK?

YOU HAD A GOOD MONTH, AL, BUT WILL IT LAST?

BILL, HOW MUCH OF AN IMPROVEMENT THIS MONTH DO WE HAVE TO *MAKE* OVER LAST MONTH'S TO DELAY THE PLANT'S CLOSING?

INCREASE YOUR BOTTOM LINE ANOTHER *FITEEN PERCENT* COMPARED TO LAST MONTH.

I THINK WE CAN DO THAT.

PLOP!

YOU--*REALLY?* FINE. DELIVER THAT, KEEP DELIVERING IT, AND WE'LL KEEP BEARINGTON OPEN.

FIFTEEN PERCENT?!?

BEARINGTO 12 MILES

EXIT 36

I'VE *GOT* TO CALL JONAH!

THAT NIGHT, ROGO REACHES JONAH IN SINGAPORE. THOUGH UNABLE TO VISIT THE PLANT, AFTER ROGO EXPLAINS THE SITUATION, JONAH HELPS HIM MAP OUT THE STRATEGY TO MOVE FORWARD.

THE FOLLOWING MORNING...

HI! I HEAR THE MEETING AT HEADQUARTERS WENT WELL.

WE'RE NOT OFF THE HOOK YET.

I TALKED TO JONAH LAST NIGHT.

AND...?

AND HE SUGGESTED WE TRY WHAT HE CALLED "THE NEXT LOGICAL STEP."

WHAT'S THAT?

CUT NON-BOTTLENECK BATCH SIZES IN HALF, AND WE'LL MAKE MORE MONEY.

WHY?

STACEY, YOU'RE INVENTORY CONTROL, YOU TELL ME.

AFTER SOME THOUGHT, STACEY SAYS THAT HALVING BATCH SIZES HALVES WORK-IN-PROGRESS, WHICH HALVES INVESTMENT IN MATERIALS, THUS IMPROVING CASH FLOW.

TO BRIEF EVERYONE WITHOUT INTERRUPTION, STACEY ARRANGES A RESTAURANT MEETING ON ROGO'S EXPENSE ACCOUNT.

Scott's CUISINE

I SPOKE TO JONAH LAST NIGHT.

QUEUE TIME IS THE MAJOR TIME FACTOR FOR PARTS GOING THROUGH THE BOTTLENECKS, AND WAIT TIME IS THE MAJOR TIME FACTOR FOR PARTS THAT DO NOT GO THROUGH BOTTLENECKS.

ROGO EXPLAINS THAT JONAH BROKE DOWN INTO **FOUR ELEMENTS** THE START-TO-FINISH TIME FOR MATERIALS ONCE THEY ARRIVE: *SET-UP*; *PROCESS TIME*; *QUEUE TIME*, AND *WAIT TIME* FOR ANOTHER ASSEMBLY PART.

ROGO CONFIRMED TO JONAH THAT THEY'VE BEEN SETTING BATCH SIZES ACCORDING TO THE *ECONOMICAL BATCH QUANTITY (EBQ)* FORMULA.

JONAH COULDN'T GO INTO DETAILS, BUT HE SAID THAT THE *EBQ* RESTS ON A NUMBER OF FLAWED ASSUMPTIONS. HE SAID TO CUT EXISTING BATCH SIZES IN HALF, WHICH WILL REDUCE BOTH QUEUE AND WAIT TIMES BY HALF, AND...

...LEAD TIME *SHRINKS*. FLOW OF PARTS INCREASES...

...CUSTOMERS GET THEIR ORDERS *FASTER*...

...WE CAN RESPOND TO MARKET CHANGES *FASTER*...

INCREASING SALES...

...AND *BONUSES!*

BUT *HALVING* BATCHES INCREASES-- COULD EVEN *DOUBLE*-- SET-UPS.

REMEMBER WHEN JONAH SAID AN HOUR LOST AT A BOTTLENECK WAS GONE FOR GOOD?

YEAH?

THE RULE JONAH GAVE ME LAST NIGHT IS THIS: AN HOUR SAVED AT A NON-BOTTLENECK IS A *MIRAGE.* HERE'S WHY:

BECAUSE BOTTLENECKS ARE SLOWER, WE ALREADY HAVE *DOWNTIME* WITH THE NON-BOTTLENECKS UNTIL THE BOTTLENECKS ARE READY FOR RESUPPLY.

EXTRA SET-UPS WILL ONLY AFFECT NON-BOTTLENECKS, EATING INTO EXISTING DOWNTIME.

111

ON MONDAY, LOU ENTERS ALEX'S OFFICE, CLOSES THE DOOR, AND ALMOST WHISPERS HIS ACCOUNTING CHANGE. INSTEAD OF USING HEADQUARTERS' 12-MONTH BASE-LINE TO CALCULATE COST OF PARTS, LOU PLANS TO ONLY USE THE PAST TWO MONTHS.

WELL, IT *IS* MORE REFLECTIVE OF PRESENT REALITY.

BUT, IT'S *HIGHLY IRREGULAR.* IF ETHAN FROST, THE HEAD OF ACCOUNTING, FINDS OUT, WE'LL BE IN *VERY* HOT WATER.

LET'S GO FOR IT.

AND ANOTHER COMPANY MYTH BITES THE DUST.

A FEW MINUTES LATER...

AL? IT'S JOHNNY JONS. BUCKY BURNSIDE'S COMPANY WANTS 1,000 MODEL 12'S. WE HAVE 50 ON INVENTORY. CAN YOU *DELIVER* 950 BY THE END OF THE MONTH?

THAT'S TWO WEEKS AWAY...

I KNOW. BUT BURNSIDE'S DESPERATE. HIS ORIGINAL SUPPLIER--OUR COMPETITOR--BOTCHED THE ORDER, DELIVERING BUPKIS IN FIVE MONTHS. CAN YOU DO IT? I NEED TO KNOW BY TOMORROW.

AND DON'T TELL ME YES IF YOU CAN'T DO IT. I'M TIRED OF BURNSIDE'S COMPLAINING ABOUT YOU NOT DELIVERING AS PROMISED.

LET ME CHECK AND I'LL GET BACK TO YOU.

ALEX INFORMS BOB, STACEY, AND RAPH ABOUT THE OPPORTUNITY. AND THEY GO TO WORK CRUNCHING NUMBERS...

IT'S TECHNICALLY FEASIBLE.

BUT ONLY IF WE WORK ON NOTHING BUT THE BURNSIDE ORDER FOR THOSE TWO WEEKS.

DON'T WANT TO DO THAT. WHAT ELSE CAN WE DO?

WELL, WE CAN HALVE THE BATCHES AGAIN.

ORDERS COULD BE RESCHEDULED TO ARRIVE ON TIME INSTEAD OF AHEAD OF SCHEDULE.

AND, BY WEEKLY AIRFREIGHTING NEEDED PARTS FROM THE VENDORS...

PLANT MANA

THEN, A WEEK AND A HALF LATER, HEADQUARTERS GETS WIND OF THE UNAUTHORIZED *ACCOUNTING* CHANGES ROGO'S INSTALLED. AN AUDITOR IS DISPATCHED.

THIS IS *HIGHLY* IRREGULAR.

NEIL, BASING COSTS ON OUR CURRENT TWO-MONTH PERIOD IS ACTUALLY A MORE TRUTHFUL REPRESENTATION.

SORRY, MR. ROGO. WE HAVE TO FOLLOW STANDARD POLICY.

BUT THE PLANT IS *DIFFERENT* NOW!

BUT THE ACCOUNTANTS ARE *UNMOVED*. ABOUT TWO WEEKS LATER, UNDER THE REIMPOSED OLD ACCOUNTING STANDARDS, INSTEAD OF THE 17 PERCENT INCREASE REVEALED BY LOU'S SYSTEM, THE INCREASE IS ONLY 12.8 PERCENT.

DAMN.

WHUP-WHUP-WHUP-WHUP

WHAT THE--?

IS THAT A *HELICOPTER*?

BUT YESTERDAY'S JOY IS A *DISTANT MEMORY* WHEN, THE NEXT MORNING IN A HEADQUARTERS' CONFERENCE ROOM, HILTON SMYTH AND THE AUDITOR ARE CALLING ALEX ROGO ON THE CARPET FOR FLOUTING THEIR PRACTICES.

WHERE'S PEACH?

HE SAID TO PROCEED WITHOUT HIM.

I WOULD LIKE TO KNOW WHY YOU ARE NOT OBSERVING PROPER PROCEDURES FOR DETERMINING ECONOMICAL BATCH QUANTITIES?

FINE. BUT BEFORE I GO INTO MY PRESENTATION, LET ME ASK THIS QUESTION: IS IT THE *GOAL* OF THE UNIWARE DIVISION TO REDUCE COSTS?

OF COURSE IT IS.

NO, ACTUALLY, THAT IS *NOT* THE GOAL. THE GOAL OF UNIWARE IS TO *MAKE MONEY.* AGREED?

THAT'S TRUE.

I'M GOING TO DEMONSTRATE THAT REGARDLESS OF WHAT OUR COSTS LOOK LIKE ACCORDING TO STANDARD MEASUREMENTS, MY PLANT HAS NEVER BEEN IN A BETTER POSITION TO MAKE MONEY NOW AND IN THE FUTURE.

ROGO THROWS DOWN THE GAUNTLET AND TELLS THEM THEIR ACCOUNTING AND PRODUCTION ASSUMPTIONS ARE WRONG. AND EVERYTHING HE'S DOING IS IN DIRECT CONTRADICTION TO ESTABLISHED RULES COMMONLY USED IN MANUFACTURING.

THE COMPANY'S RULES ARE:

· BALANCE CAPACITY WITH DEMAND, THEN TRY TO MAINTAIN THE FLOW.

· EVERY WORK CENTER STANDS ON ITS OWN. TO KEEP EFFICIENCIES HIGH, STRIVE TO KEEP ALL PEOPLE AND MACHINES WORKING ALL THE TIME.

· AN--*INCORRECT*-- ASSUMPTION THAT UTILIZATION AND ACTIVATION ARE THE SAME.

ROGO THEN PROCEEDS TO SHOOT EACH RULE DOWN.

INSTEAD OF BALANCING CAPACITY, THEY NEED *EXCESS* CAPACITY. THEY SHOULD BALANCE THE FLOW WITH THE DEMAND, NOT THE CAPACITY.

ONLY THE BOTTLENECKS SHOULD BE ACTIVATED TO THEIR FULL CAPACITY. THE LEVEL OF ACTIVATION OF ALL OTHER WORK CENTERS SHOULD NOT BE DETERMINED BY THEIR OWN CAPACITY, BUT BY SOME OTHER CONSTRAINT IN THE SYSTEM.

ACTIVATING A RESOURCE AND *UTILIZING* A RESOURCE ARE *NOT* SYNONYMOUS.

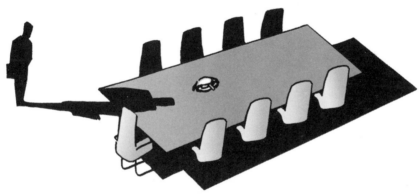

HELLO, AL, I KNEW YOU'D WANT TO SEE ME. TAKE A SEAT.

HILTON SMYTH IS GOING TO SUBMIT A *NEGATIVE REPORT* ABOUT MY PLANT, AND YOU NEED TO HEAR MY SIDE.

THE RECAPPING TAKES JUST A FEW MINUTES.

AND HILTON'S RESPONSE TO YOUR EXPLANATION WAS?

HE BASICALLY *REFUSED* TO LISTEN.

HE CONTINUES TO CLAIM THAT AS LONG AS COST OF PRODUCTS INCREASE, PROFITS EVENTUALLY HAVE TO GO DOWN.

DON'T YOU THINK HE HAS A POINT?

NO, I DON'T.

AS LONG AS I KEEP MY COSTS UNDER CONTROL AND JOHNNY JONS HAPPY, PROFITS CAN ONLY GO *UP.*

FINE.

MEG, CAN YOU CALL HILTON, ETHAN, AND JOHNNY JONS IN HERE, PLEASE?

WHAT'S GOING ON, BILL?

DON'T WORRY, JUST WAIT AND SEE.

A FEW MINUTES LATER...

HILTON, YOU'VE HEARD ALEX'S REPORT AND SEEN HIS PLANT'S FINANCIAL RESULTS. AS DIVISION PRODUCTIVITY MANAGER AND A FELLOW PLANT MANAGER,

WHAT'S YOUR RECOMMENDATION?

ALEX SHOULD BE CALLED TO ORDER. PLANT PRODUCTIVITY IS DETERIORATING, COST OF PRODUCTS IS GOING UP, PROPER PROCEDURES ARE NOT BEING FOLLOWED. *IMMEDIATE ACTIONS* ARE IN ORDER.

WHAT'S YOUR TAKE, FROST?

WELL, IN THE LAST TWO MONTHS THE PLANT'S BEEN PROFITABLE, RELEASING A LOT OF CASH FOR THE DIVISION.

A TEMPORARY PHENOMENON. WE MUST EXPECT *BIG LOSSES* IN ALEX'S PLANT SOON.

JOHNNY? COMMENTS?

BEARINGTON IS THE ONLY ONE THAT CAN PRODUCE MIRACLES. YOU'VE ALL HEARD ABOUT BURNSIDE'S VISIT. WITH ALEX'S PLANT WE CAN BLAST THE MARKET.

BUT AT *WHAT PRICE?* CUTTING BATCHES FAR BELOW OPTIMUM SIZE... DEVOTING THE ENTIRE PLANT TO ONE ORDER... THINK OF THE LONG-TERM RAMIFICATIONS!

I NEVER DEVOTED THE ENTIRE PLANT TO ONE ORDER! I HAVE NO PAST-DUE ORDERS. ALL MY CLIENTS ARE PLEASED.

MIRACLES EXIST ONLY IN FAIRY TALES.

SO WHAT'S THE VERDICT--IS MY PLANT GOING TO BE CLOSED?

TRAVEL

PARKI

CREDIT

128

THE 5 FOCUSING STEPS OF THE THEORY OF CONSTRAINTS

1. *IDENTIFY* THE SYSTEM'S CONSTRAINT(S).

2. DECIDE HOW TO *EXPLOIT* THE SYSTEM'S CONSTRAINT(S).

3. *SUBORDINATE* EVERYTHING ELSE TO THE ABOVE DECISION(S).

4. *ELEVATE* THE SYSTEM'S CONSTRAINT(S).

5. *GO BACK* TO STEP 1.
   WARNING: DO NOT ALLOW INERTIA TO CAUSE A SYSTEM'S CONSTRAINT.